ENOUGH IS ENOUGH LO ⌐⌐⌐⌐⌐⌐

ISBN 0-929097-01-7

LO-BOY GOLFTOONS NORTH AMERICA INC.
500 Capitol of Texas Hwy.
Building 3, Suite 200
Austin, Texas
78746

#1-8307 – 124th St.
Surrey, B.C., Canada
V3W 9G2

1

INTRODUCTION

A little golf tee may look cute and totally harmless to you . . . . but have you ever sat on one? . . . . No? . . . . Well I have, many times! Just picture yourself on a barstool. Daydreaming. All of a sudden somebody sneaks up on you and hits you off the stool with a sledgehammer. Stars are dancing in front of your eyes. How would you like that, I ask you. Who asks us if we like it? If you are a golfer or on your way to becoming one, we golfballs ask you from our bottom to our hearts, put yourself in our helpless position and have mercy on us!

Hundreds of books have been written about golf. Golf instructions, golf manners, golf tips, golf humour but no book has ever been written about the plight of the endless suffering little golfball. We live in a time of bleeding hearts, nature lovers and other do gooders but who ever shows concern for us? It is high time somebody did. If we ever decide to protest, go on strike and marches, you're in big trouble. Ever try playing golf without us? Golfballs of the world, unite!

I apologize to my little dimpled friends for mistreating, wounding, blaming and embarrassing them for my mistakes. For letting them drown or choke in the mud. Please forgive me, I didn't mean to.

"I DON'T CARE, BUT IN THIS COUNTRY WE BUCKLE UP!"

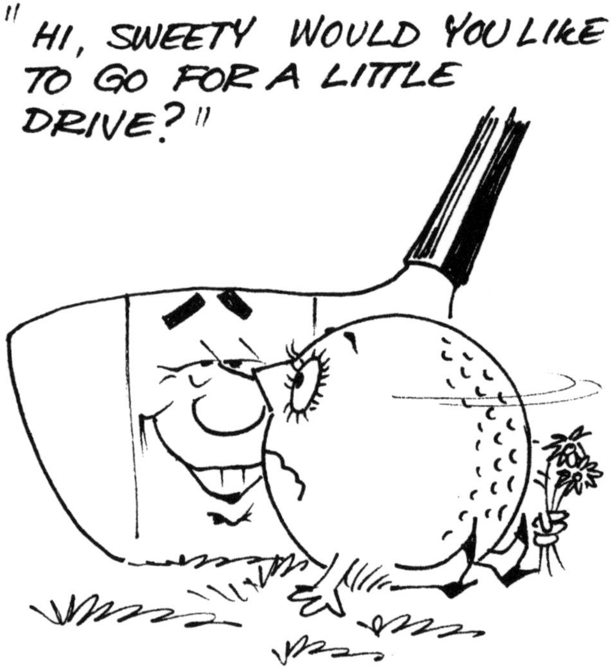
"HI, SWEETY WOULD YOU LIKE TO GO FOR A LITTLE DRIVE?"

9

13

"GOLF ISN'T LIFE AND DEATH TO THEM...
...IT'S MUCH MORE!"

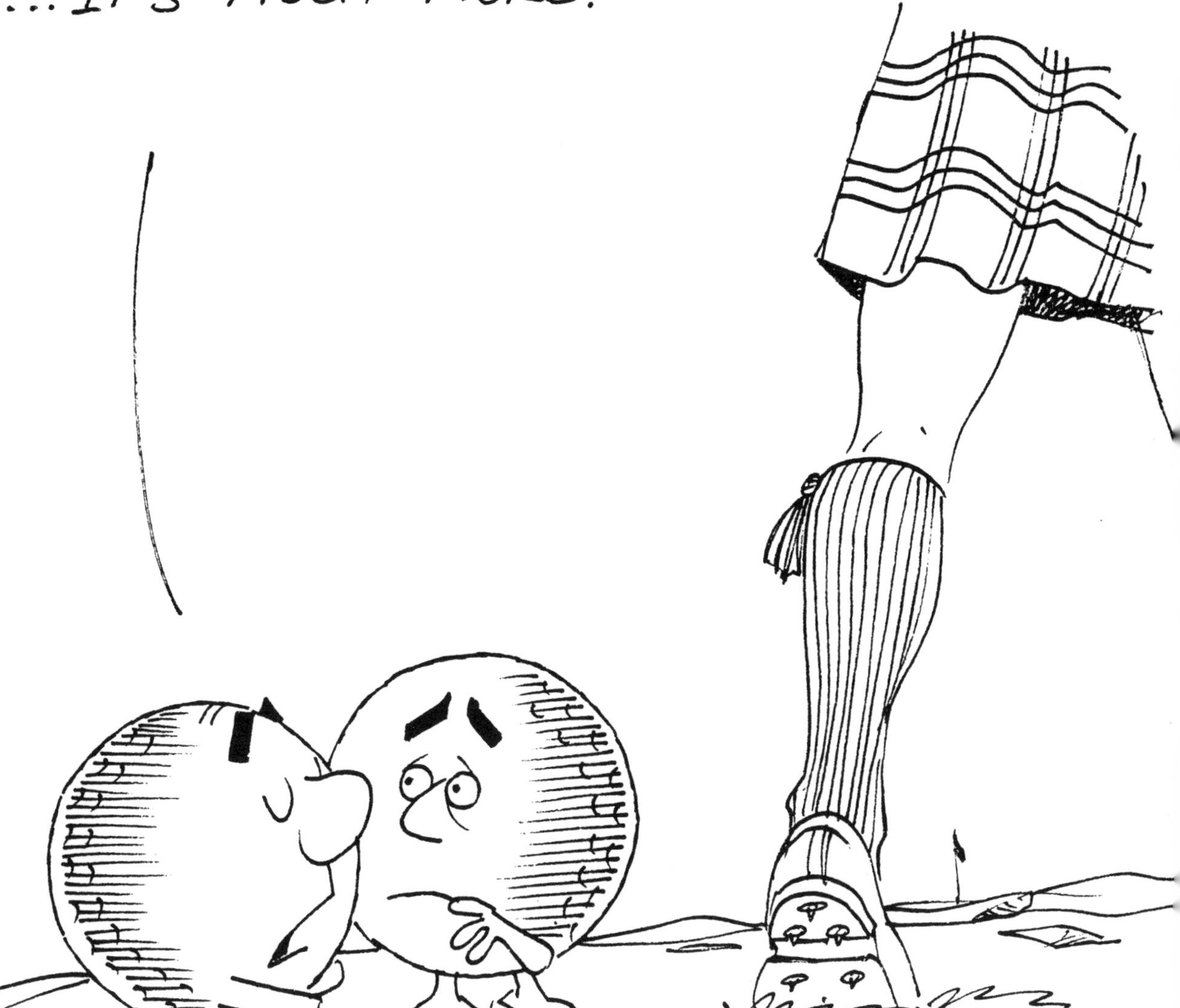

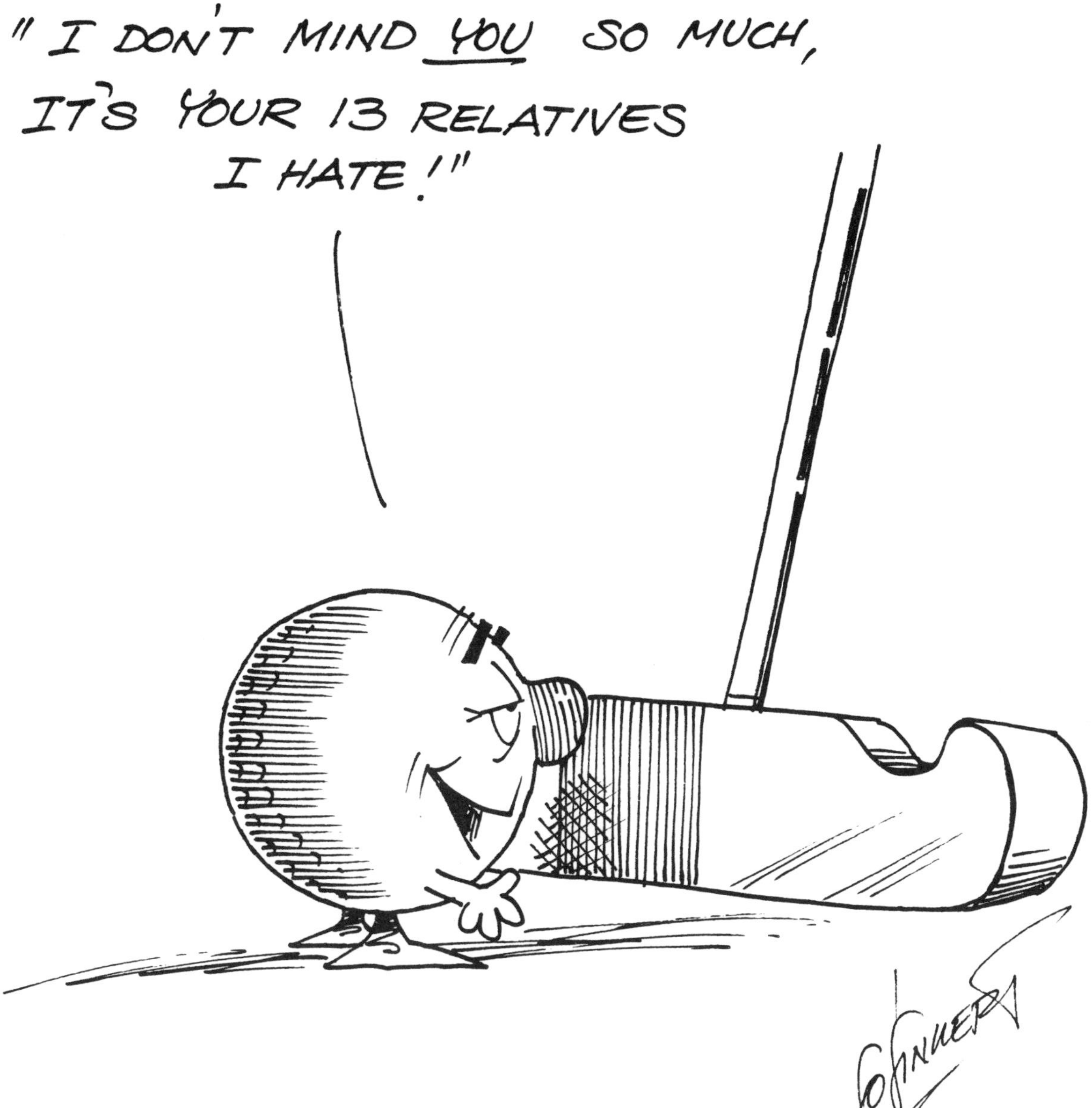
"I DON'T MIND YOU SO MUCH, IT'S YOUR 13 RELATIVES I HATE!"

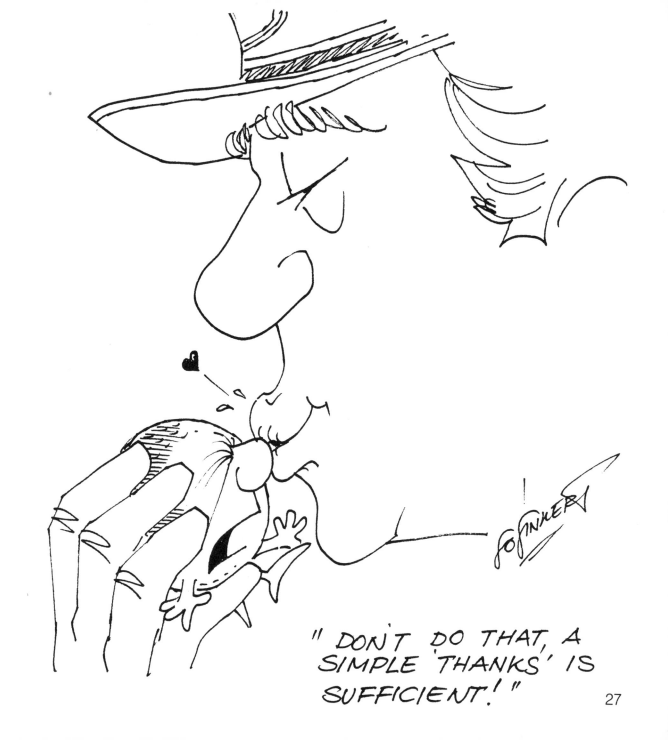

"DON'T DO THAT, A SIMPLE 'THANKS' IS SUFFICIENT!"

27

"NO, I DIDN'T DUCK, YOU LOOKED UP!"

"ALL I GET OUT OF THIS GAME IS A BIG BANG!"

33

39

43

47

55

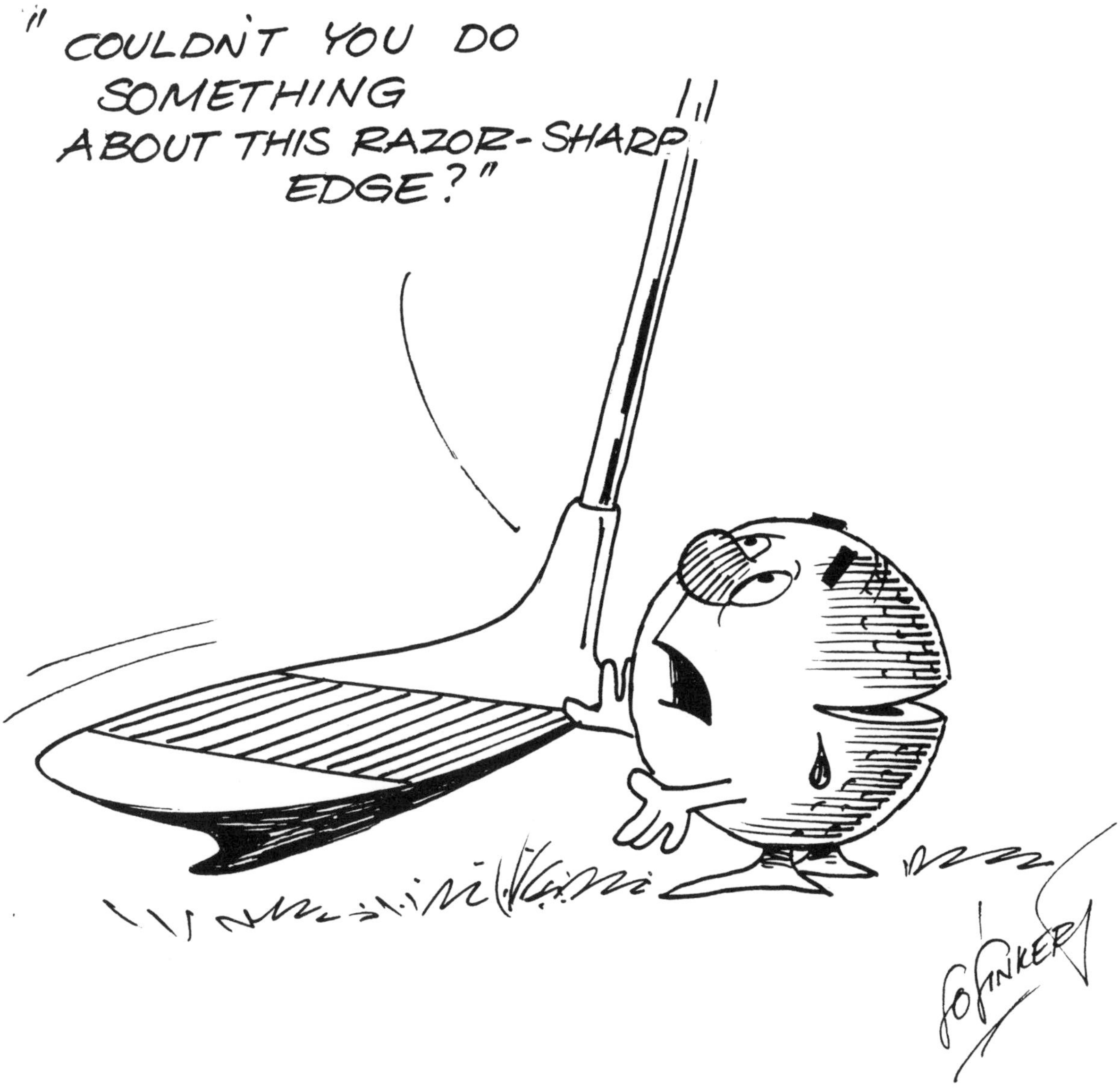
"COULDN'T YOU DO SOMETHING ABOUT THIS RAZOR-SHARP EDGE?"

"I'D PREFER BEING ADDRESSED WITH 'LITTLE SONNY BOY' NOT LITTLE S.O.B.!"

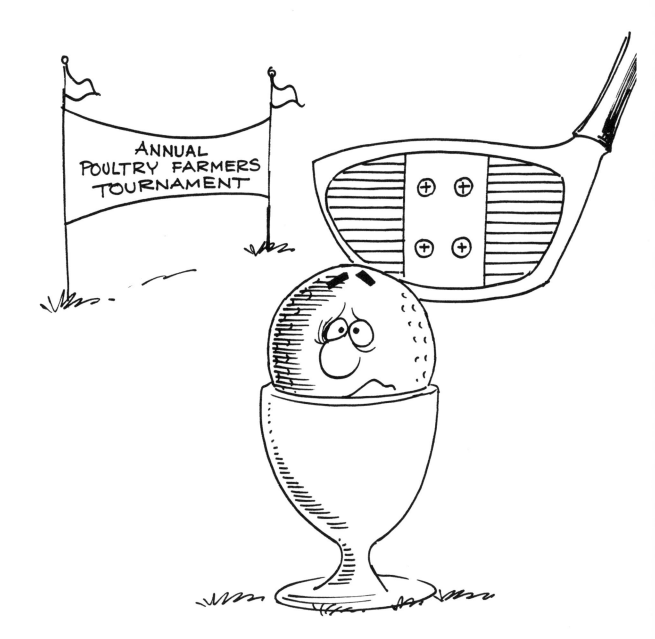

"WHAT DO YOU MEAN WHERE IS THE GOAL, ... IS THIS YOUR FIRST GAME?"

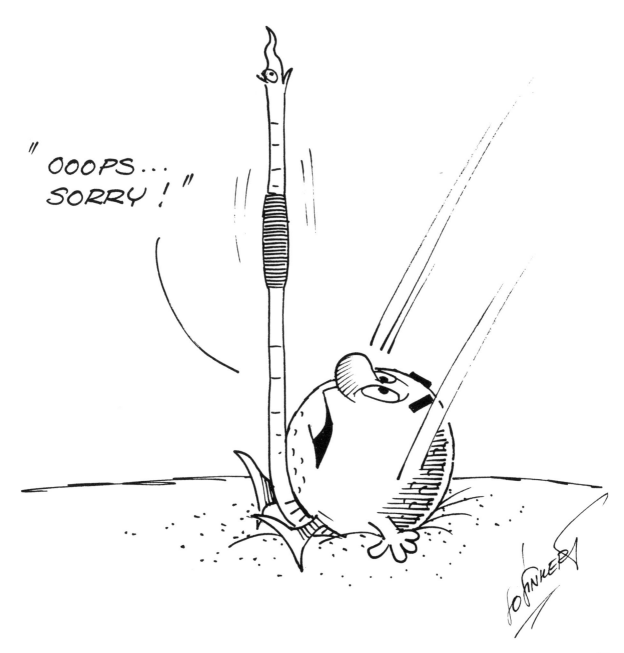

63

" WHAT DO YOU MEAN THIS WASN'T YOUR DAY... HAVE YOU PLAYED THIS GAME BEFORE?"
18

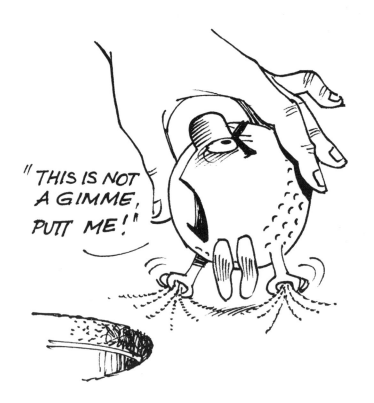

67

"HOLD IT, I FORGOT MY FLIGHT TICKET!"

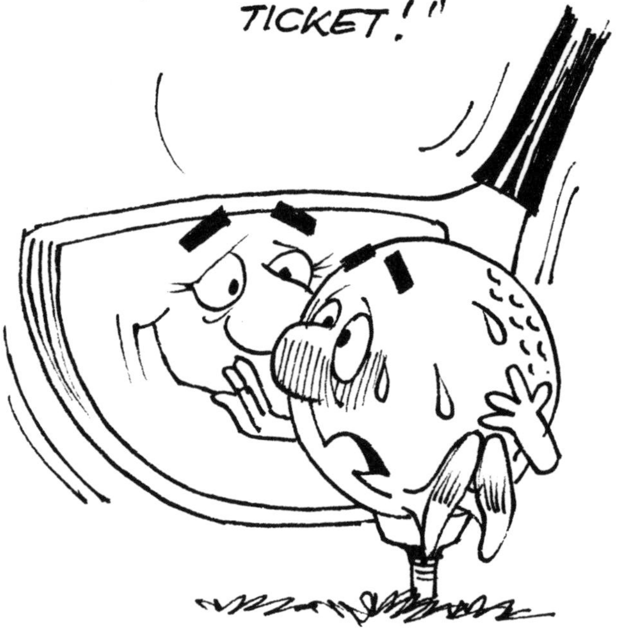

"WHY DON'T YOU PICK ON SOMEONE YOUR OWN SIZE?"

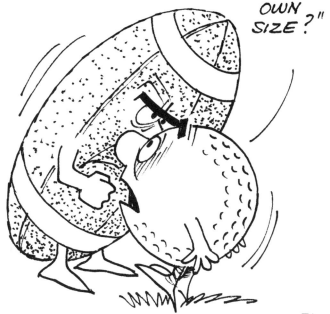

"PEOPLE BEAT ME ALL DAY LONG, NEVER A HUG OR A COMPLIMENT!"

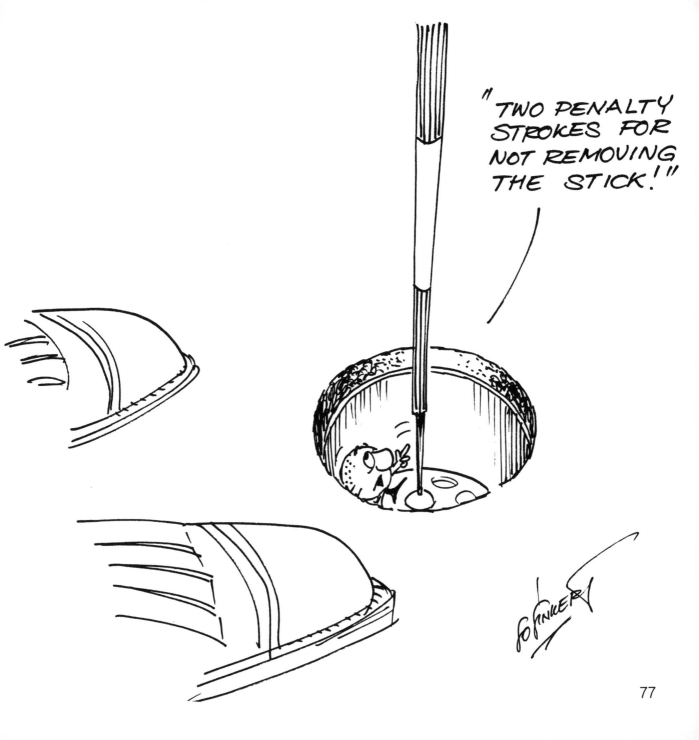

"OH MY GOD, PREGNANT SHE WAS TOO!"

89